HIGHTREE
PUBLISHING

THIS BOOK IS DEDICATED TO CHILDREN EVERYWHERE.
MAY YOU ALWAYS USE YOUR VOICE.
MAY YOU ALWAYS MAKE GOOD TROUBLE.
−V.A.

TO MY GRANDFATHER, WHO ALSO LOVED TO DRAW.
−F.F.

Edited by Hathaway Pogue • Copyedited by Valerie Press

YOU HAVE A
VOICE

WRITTEN BY
VERA AHIYYA

ILLUSTRATED BY
FABIANA FAIALLO

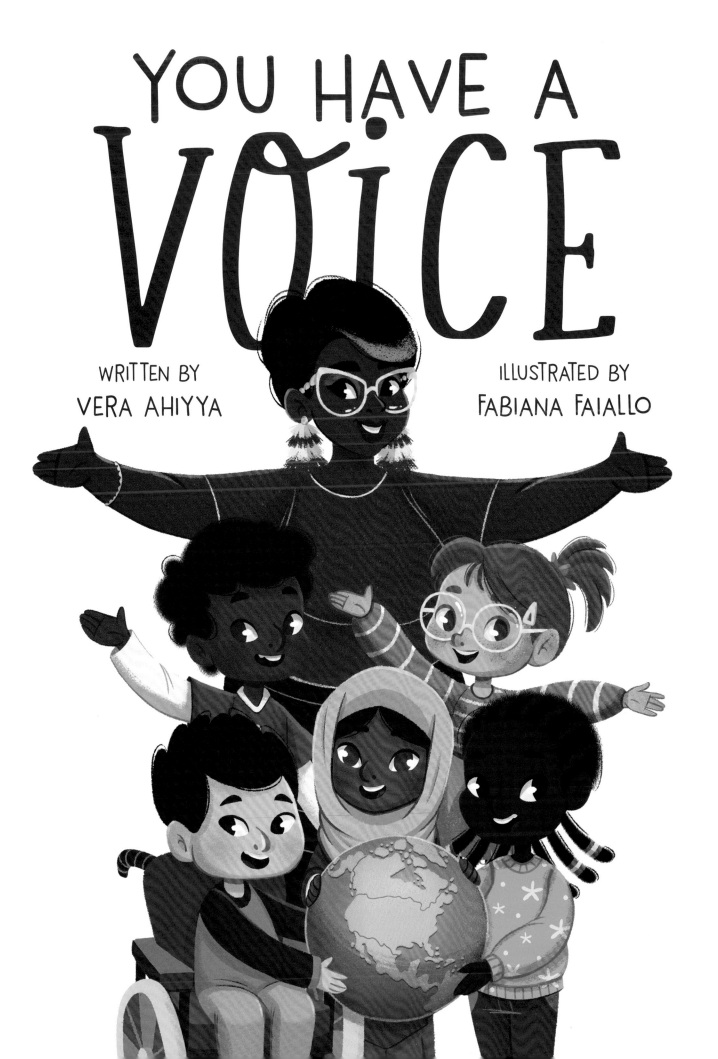

Dear friends, before I send you
off to start your work and play,

I think it's important for
me to talk to you today.

Remember our words about equality,
justice, and skin color,

MARTIN LUTHER KING JR.

MALALA YOUSAFZAI

ROSA PARKS

SONIA SOTOMAYOR

RUTH BADER GINSBURG

fairness, gender, hope, and respect for one another?

AUTUMN PELTIER

MARSHA P. JOHNSON

MOTHER TERESA

STOP
STOP STOP

GARRETT MORGAN

MAE JEMISON

Well, today we need to talk about
something that is like a disease.

It's not something you can catch,
I hope that puts your mind at ease

Some people believe that
certain skin colors

should not have the same rights
or privileges as others.

I bet you are thinking,
'WOW, that's not fair!'
'What's this thing called?'
'We need to be aware!'

This belief is called racism.
Racism is wrong,

and we need to work to end it. It's
been around much too long.

You know what's right, you know what's wrong,
you have a voice, so

SPEAK UP,

BE STRONG!

By now, you'd think something
so terrible would have gone away.
Racism is everywhere and
seems to want to stay.

Here's the good news; you can fix
things but it won't always be easy.

Speaking up is always right, I
want you to believe me.

You have to start somewhere
and you have to start today,

because treating others unfairly
is not the way to play.

You know what's right, you know what's wrong,
you have a voice, so

SPEAK UP,

BE STRONG!

When someone is being treated differently
because of the color of their skin,
speak up, say 'Stop!' 'This isn't right!'
'I won't let racism win.'

Write a letter, make a sign, talk to your family.
March together and create the world that you want to see.

Even children as young as you
can use your voice to make a difference,

THAT'S HUGE!

You know what's right, you know what's wrong,

you have a voice, so

SPEAK UP,
BE STRONG!

The best way for things to change
is to speak up for what's right, at any age.

Use your mind, listen to your heart,
work together, do your part.

You know what's right, you know what's wrong,
you have a voice, so

SPEAK UP,

BE STRONG!

The choice to make a difference is up to you.